Ready to Read
Alphabet

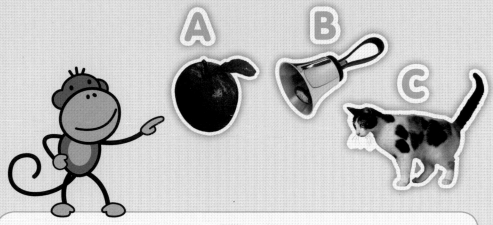

How to Play

1. Press the Power button to turn the SD-X Reader on or off. The LED will light up when the SD-X Reader is on.

2. Touch the volume buttons found on this page to adjust the volume.

3. Touch words and pictures on the page to hear audio. The monkey gives instructions and starts activities.

4. After two minutes of inactivity, the SD-X Reader will beep and go to sleep.

5. If the batteries are low, the SD-X Reader will beep twice and the LED will start blinking. Replace the batteries by following the instructions on the next page. The SD-X Reader uses two AAA batteries.

6. To use headphones or earbuds, plug them into the headphone jack on the SD-X Reader.

Volume

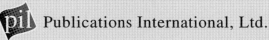

pil Publications International, Ltd.

Battery Information
Includes two replaceable AAA batteries (UM-4 or LR03).

Battery Installation
1. Open battery door with small flat-head or Phillips screwdriver.
2. Install new batteries according to +/- polarity. If batteries are not installed properly, the device will not function.
3. Replace battery door; secure with small screw.

Battery Safety
Batteries must be replaced by adults only. Properly dispose of used batteries. See battery manufacturer for disposal recommendations. Do not mix alkaline, standard (carbon-zinc), or rechargeable (nickel-cadmium) batteries. Do not mix old and new batteries. Only recommended batteries of the same or equivalent type should be used. Remove weakened or dead batteries. Never short-circuit the supply terminals. Non-rechargeable batteries are not to be recharged. Do not use rechargeable batteries. If batteries are swallowed, in the USA, promptly see a doctor and have the doctor phone 1-202-625-3333 collect. In other countries, have the doctor call your local poison control center. This product uses 2 AAA batteries (2 X 1.5V = 3.0 V). Use batteries of the same or equivalent type as recommended. The supply terminals are not to be short-circuited. Batteries should be changed when sounds mix, distort, or become otherwise unintelligible as batteries weaken. The electrostatic discharge may interfere with the sound module. If this occurs, please simply restart the sound module by pressing any key.

In Europe, the dustbin symbol indicates that batteries, rechargeable batteries, button cells, battery packs, and similar materials must not be discarded in household waste. Batteries containing hazardous substances are harmful to the environment and to health. Please help to protect the environment from health risks by telling your children to dispose of batteries properly and by taking batteries to local collection points. Batteries handled in this manner are safely recycled.

Warning: Changes or modifications to this unit not expressly approved by the party responsible for compliance could void the user's authority to operate the equipment.

NOTE: This equipment has been tested and found to comply with the limits for a Class B digital device, pursuant to Part 15 of the FCC Rules. These limits are designed to provide reasonable protection against harmful interference in a residential installation. This equipment generates, uses, and can radiate radio frequency energy and, if not installed and used in accordance with the instructions, may cause harmful interference to radio communications. However, there is no guarantee that interference will not occur in a particular installation. If this equipment does cause harmful interference to radio or television reception, which can be determined by turning the equipment off and on, the user is encouraged to try to correct the interference by one or more of the following measures: Reorient or relocate the receiving antenna. Increase the separation between the equipment and receiver. Connect the equipment into an outlet on a circuit different from that to which the receiver is connected. Consult the dealer or an experienced radio TV technician for help.

Contributing Writers: Natalie Goldstein, Anne Schreiber, Kristen Walsky, Michele Warrence-Schreiber

Consultants: Susan A. Miller, Ed.D., Dr. Leslie Ann Perry, Dr. Elizabeth C. Stull

Illustrators: Nicholas Myers, James Schlottman, George Ulrich

Picture Credits: Comstock RF; Corbis RF; Image Club Graphics; PhotoDisc; PIL Collection; StockByte

Copyright © 2011 Publications International, Ltd.
Product and sound element design, engineering, and reproduction are proprietary technologies of Publications International, Ltd.

All rights reserved. This publication may not be reproduced in whole or in part by any means whatsoever without written permission from:

Louis Weber, C.E.O., Publications International, Ltd.
7373 North Cicero Avenue
Lincolnwood, Illinois 60712

Ground Floor, 59 Gloucester Place
London W1U 8JJ

Customer Service:
1-888-724-0144 or customer_service@pilbooks.com
www.pilbooks.com

SD-X Interactive is a registered trademark in the United States and Canada.

Manufactured in China.

8 7 6 5 4 3 2 1
ISBN-10: 1-4508-2066-2
ISBN-13: 978-1-4508-2066-0

A, B, C, D, E, F

Recognize uppercase letters A, B, C, D, E, F.

A B C

Cat

Apple

Ball

D E F

G, H, I, J, K

Recognize uppercase letters G, H, I, J, K.

G	G	A
H	E	H
I	I	C
J	J	Z
K	K	T

L, M, N, O, P

Q, R, S, T, U

Recognize uppercase letters Q, R, S, T, U.

 Q

 U

 R

 T

 S

 R

 T

 S

 U

 Q

V, W, X, Y, Z

V	P	V
W	W	D
X	Q	X

A to Z

Use alphabetical order.

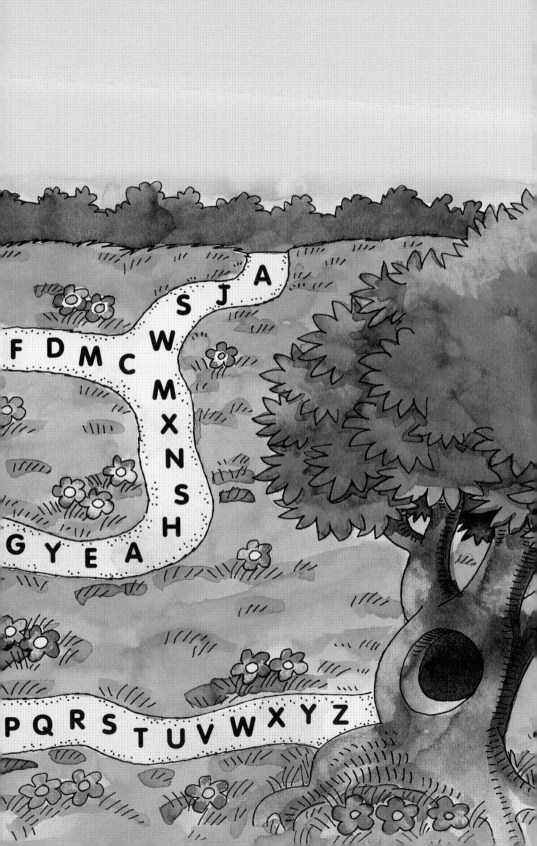

What Comes Next?

Use alphabetical order.

B C

D E ___

G ___ I J

___ L M

A F H K

N O

Q R T

U V

X Z

P S W Y

Balloon, Balloon

Match uppercase and lowercase letters.

Family Reunion

Match uppercase and lowercase letters.

d   E

e   F

f   D

Ice Cream!

Match uppercase and lowercase letters.

Lock and Key

Match uppercase and lowercase letters.

Make a Match

Match uppercase and lowercase letters.

Time to Paint

Match uppercase and lowercase letters.

 P

 q

 Q

 r

 R

 p

Tic-Tac-Toe

Match uppercase and lowercase letters.

s	f	s
t	t	d
u	u	m

Uu	By	Qi
Am	Tt	Pr
Dc	Hg	Ss

Time to Pack!

Work with Vv and Ww.

 **Van**	 **Wagon**

whale

violin

vase

watch

Driving the Alphabet

Match uppercase and lowercase letters.

x y z

Letter Scramble

Match uppercase and lowercase letters.

D	f
T	h
N	t
H	d
F	n

J	q
G	a
Q	j
A	r
R	g

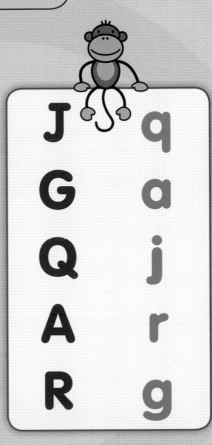

Lowercase Letter Train

Recognize lowercase letters; use alphabetical order.

o u l c f x i r

Who Comes First?

Sequence words in alphabetical order.